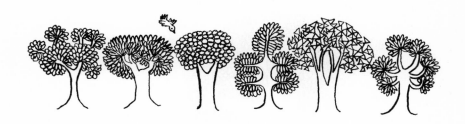

In the Middle of the Trees

Books By Karla Kuskin

ROAR AND MORE
JAMES AND THE RAIN
IN THE MIDDLE OF THE TREES

IN THE
MIDDLE OF
THE TREES

by
KARLA KUSKIN

HARPER & BROTHERS
PUBLISHERS NEW YORK

IN THE MIDDLE OF THE TREES
Copyright © 1958 by Karla Kuskin
Printed in the United States of America

All rights in this book are reserved.

Library of Congress catalog card number: 58-5291

FOR CHARLIE

VERY EARLY

When I wake in the early mist
The sun has hardly shown
And everything is still asleep
And I'm awake alone.
The stars are faint and flickering.
The sun is new and shy.
And all the world sleeps quietly,
Except the sun and I.
And then beginning noises start,
The whrrrs and huffs and hums,
The birds peep out to find a worm,
The mice squeak out for crumbs,
The calf moos out to find the cow,
And taste the morning air
And everything is wide awake
And running everywhere.
The dew has dried,
The fields are warm,
The day is loud and bright,
And I'm the one who woke the sun
And kissed the stars good night.

WHEN I WENT OUT

When I went out to see the sun
There wasn't sun or anyone
But there was only sand and sea
And lots of rain that fell on me
And where the rain and river met
The water got completely wet.

8

SITTING IN THE SAND

Sitting in the sand and the sea comes up
So you put your hands together
And you use them like a cup
And you dip them in the water
With a scooping kind of motion
And before the sea goes out again
You have a sip of ocean.

SPRING

I'm shouting
I'm singing
I'm swinging through trees
I'm winging skyhigh
With the buzzing black bees.
I'm the sun
I'm the moon
I'm the dew on the rose.
I'm a rabbit
Whose habit
Is twitching his nose.
I'm lively
I'm lovely
I'm kicking my heels.
I'm crying "Come dance"
To the fresh water eels.
I'm racing through meadows
Without any coat
I'm a gamboling lamb
I'm a light leaping goat
I'm a bud
I'm a bloom
I'm a dove on the wing.
I'm running on rooftops
And welcoming spring!

THE BALLOON

I went to the park
And I bought a balloon.
It sailed through the sky
Like a large orange moon.
It bumped and it fluttered
And swam with the clouds.
Small birds flew around it
In high chirping crowds.
It bounced and it balanced
And bowed with the breeze.
It skimmed past the leaves
On the tops of the trees.
And then as the day
Started turning to night
I gave a short jump
And I held the string tight
And home we all sailed
Through the darkening sky,
The orange balloon, the small birds
And I.

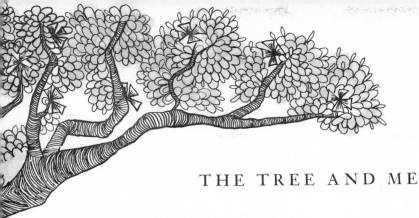

THE TREE AND ME

There's a tree by the meadow
By the sand by the sea
On a hillock near a valley
That belongs to me
With small spring leaves
Like small green dimes
That cast their shadows on the grass
A thousand separate times
With round brown branches
Like outstretched sleeves
And the twigs come out as fingers
And the fingers hold the leaves
With blossoms here and there
And always pink and soft and stout
And when the blossoms disappear
The apples hurry out
And
In the middle of the blossoms
In the center of the tree
With a hat and coat of leaves on
Sits smiling me.

THE SNAKE

A snake slipped through the thin green grass
A silver snake
I watched it pass
It moved like a ribbon
Silent as snow.
I think it smiled
As it passed my toe.

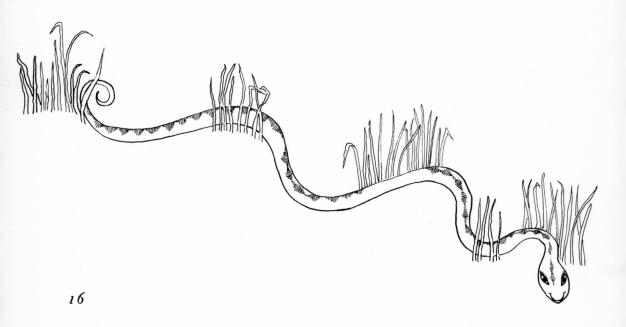

THE HAT

Somebody gave me a hat.
It has three feathers and it's sort of flat.
I tried it on my brother.
I tried it on the cat.
And then I tried it on myself.
It looked too fat.
You may have it
If you'd like it.
It's a sort of fat flat hat.

THE QUESTION

People always say to me
"What do you think you'd like to be
When you grow up?"
And I say "Why,
I think I'd like to be the sky
Or be a plane or train or mouse
Or maybe be a haunted house
Or something furry, rough and wild . . .
Or maybe I will stay a child."

THE THINGS I DO

I'm very good at climbing
I nearly climbed a tree
But just as I was almost up
I sort of skinned my knee.

I'm wonderful at walking
I almost walked a mile
But when I got around the block
I rested for a while.

I'm excellent at swimming
Though I'm not very old
I almost swam the ocean
But the water was too cold.

But what I'm really best at
Is skipping down the hall.
I'm very good at skipping.
I'm wonderful at skipping.
I'm marvelous at skipping,
That is unless I fall.

TIPTOE

Yesterday I skipped all day,
The day before I ran,
Today I'm going to tiptoe
Everywhere I can.
I'll tiptoe down the stairway.
I'll tiptoe through the door.
I'll tiptoe to the living room
And give an awful roar
And my father, who is reading,
Will jump up from his chair
And mumble something silly like
"I didn't see you there."
I'll tiptoe to my mother
And give a little cough
And when she spins to see me
Why, I'll softly tiptoe off.
I'll tiptoe through the meadows,
Over hills and yellow sands
And when my toes get tired
Then I'll tiptoe on my hands.

FALL

When I go walking in the fall
I stop to watch the deer.
They open up their lovely eyes
And blink
And disappear.
The rabbits hop from here
To there
And in
And out
And under
While deep within the forest heart
The black bears roar like thunder.
The chipmunks gather butternuts
And hide them in a tree
Where clever squirrels
Discover them
And laugh with squirrelish glee.
My hat is green
My jacket blue
With patches on the sleeves
And as I walk
I crunch through piles
Of red and yellow leaves.

FULL OF THE MOON

It's full of the moon
The dogs dance out
Through brush and bush and bramble.
They howl and yowl
And growl and prowl.
They amble, ramble, scramble.
They rush through brush.
They push through bush.
They yip and yap and hurr.
They lark around and bark around
With prickles in their fur.
They two-step in the meadow.
They polka on the lawn.
Tonight's the night
The dogs dance out
And chase their tails till dawn.

THE GOLD-TINTED DRAGON

What's the good of a wagon
Without any dragon
To pull you for mile after mile?
An elegant lean one
A gold-tinted green one
Wearing a dragonly smile.
You'll sweep down the valleys
You'll sail up the hills
Your dragon will shine in the sun
And as you rush by
The people will cry
"I wish that my wagon had one!"

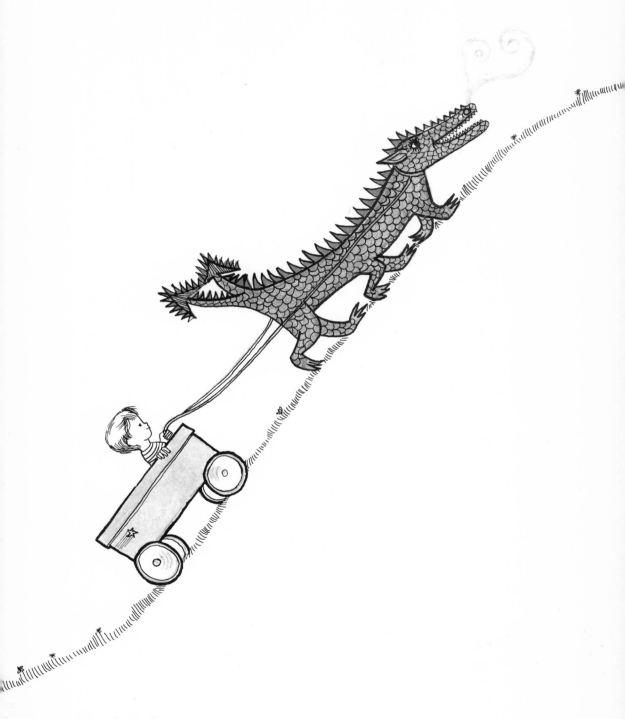

LEWIS HAS A TRUMPET

A trumpet
A trumpet
Lewis has a trumpet
A bright one that's yellow
A loud proud horn.
He blows it in the evening
When the moon is newly rising
He blows it when it's raining
In the cold and misty morn
It honks and it whistles
It roars like a lion
It rumbles like a lion
With a wheezy huffing hum
His parents say it's awful
Oh really simply awful
But
Lewis says he loves it
It's such a handsome trumpet
And when he's through with trumpets
He's going to buy a drum.

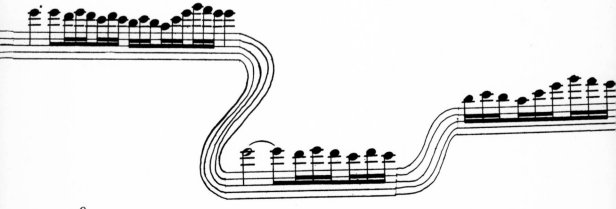

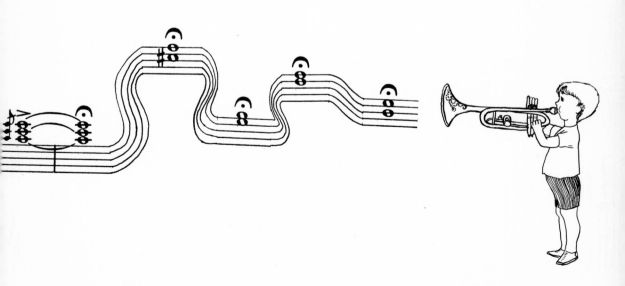

CATHERINE

Catherine said "I think I'll bake
A most delicious chocolate cake."
She took some mud and mixed it up
While adding water from a cup
And then some weeds and nuts and bark
And special gravel from the park
A thistle and a dash of sand.
She beat out all the lumps by hand.
And on the top she wrote "To You"
The way she says the bakers do
And then she signed it "Fondly C."
And gave the whole of it to me.
I thanked her but I wouldn't dream
Of eating cake without ice cream.

SWEET DELILAH

A cat named Sweet Delilah
Who loved her daily milk
Used to sit and lick her fur
Until she looked like silk.
Her nose was pink and little.
She kept her whiskers nice.
Her paws were clean.
Her eyes were green.
She wasn't rude to mice.
From miles around the people came
To watch her winning ways
And they had nought to say but good
And nought to give but praise.
"A model cat, Delilah"
They used to say
And bow.
But yet it was the sober truth
She couldn't say meow.
She couldn't say meow at all
Or even just me-ew
Instead she'd give a half a bark
And then a half harroo.
A chilling noise

A shrilling noise
A noise to start a riot
But she was such a model cat
She usually kept quiet.
One day a pack of hungry wolves
Came sweeping into town.
Their coats were salt and pepper gray
And very tangled brown
And when Delilah saw them
She opened up her mouth
And gave a barking loud harroo
That rang out north and south.
It rang out east,
It rang out west,
It rang out up and down
And people came with pitchforks
From many miles around.
They yelled "Shoo wolves
Yes, all you wolves"
And ran them out of town.
And when the fight was over
And each man embraced his wife
They gave Delilah catnip
And cream enough for life.

AROUND AND AROUND

The flower's on the bird
Which is underneath the bee
And the bird is on the kitten
On the cat on me.
I'm on a chair
On some grass
On a lawn
And the lawn is on a meadow
And the world is what it's on.
And all of us together
When the day is nearly done
Like to sit and watch the weather
As we spin around the sun.

THE SEASONS

The leaves have left without a warning
I noticed when I woke this morning.
The spring arrived and then it went.
The summer came and now it's spent.
The leaves turned yellow, crimson, brown
And drifted, sifted slowly down.
And now the trees look bare and thin
It's time for winter to begin
And make their branches thick with snow
Because that's how the seasons go.

SNOW

We'll play in the snow
And stray in the snow
And stay in the snow
In a snow-white park.
We'll clown in the snow
And frown in the snow
Fall down in the snow
Till it's after dark.
We'll cook snow pies
In a big snow pan.
We'll make snow eyes
In a round snow man.
We'll sing snow songs
And chant snow chants
And roll in the snow
In our fat snow pants.
And when it's time to go home to eat
We'll have snow toes
On our frosted feet.

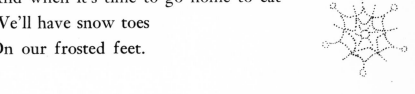

THE MIDDLE OF THE NIGHT

This is a song to be sung at night
When nothing is left of you and the light
When the cats don't bark
And the mice don't moo
And the nightmares come and nuzzle you
When there's blackness in the cupboards
And the closet and the hall
And a tipping, tapping, rapping
In the middle of the wall
When the lights have one by one gone out
All over everywhere
And a shadow by the curtains
Bumps a shadow by the chair
Then you hide beneath your pillow
With your eyes shut very tight
And you sing
"There's nothing sweeter than
The middle of the night.
I'm extremely fond of shadows
And I really must confess
That cats and bats don't scare me
Well, they couldn't scare me less
And most of all I like the things
That slide and slip and creep."
It really is surprising
How fast you fall asleep.